THE
COPS 'N' ROBBERS
JOKE BOOK

Laura Norder

Illustrated by William Kevans

Hippo Books
Scholastic Publications Limited
London

Scholastic Publications Ltd.,
10 Earlham Street, London WC2H 9RX, UK

Scholastic Inc.,
730 Broadway, New York, NY 10003, USA

Scholastic Tab Publications Ltd.,
123 Newkirk Road, Richmond Hill,
Ontario L4C 3G5, Canada

Ashton Scholastic Pty. Ltd.,
P O Box 579, Gosford, New South Wales,
Australia

Ashton Scholastic Ltd.,
165 Marua Road, Panmure, Auckland 6,
New Zealand

First published by Scholastic Publications Limited, 1990

Text copyright © Mary Douglas, 1990
Illustration copyright © William Kevans

ISBN 0 590 76315 6

Welcome to Nickem Nick, where Detective Golightly, P.C. Pouncer, W.P.C. Perfect and Woofer the police dog spend their time trying to catch criminals – and Burglar Bill, Smasher Smith and Sneaky Sid spend their time trying not to get caught!

W.P.C. PERFECT: Own up now! Did you steal that 3-kilo tin of toffees from the sweetshop?
SAMMY: *Mmmmmmmmmmmmmmmmmm-grrrrh!*

What do you get if you cross a policeman and a telegram?
Copper wire.

P.C. POUNCER: I got a puncture in the front tyre of my bike yesterday.
W.P.C. PERFECT: *Did you fix it?*
P.C. POUNCER: No, I just raised the saddle.

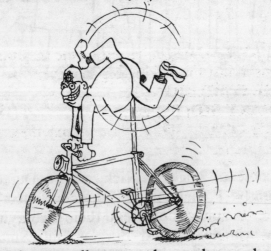

What do you call a man who steals your beer?
Nick MacGuinness.

JUDGE WRIGHT: Do you plead guilty or not guilty?
BURGLAR BILL: *I'll tell you once I've heard the evidence.*

How do policemen patrol the seabed?
In squid cars.

W.P.C. PERFECT: Why did you run away after you'd kicked your ball through the sweetshop window?
SALLY: *Because I couldn't bear to see it going through all that pane.*

SNEAKY SID: 'You're telling me they put you in prison just for making big money?
MIKE O'MILLION: *Yes.*
SNEAKY SID: But why?
MIKE O'MILLION: *It was about three centimetres too big all round.*

FLORIST: Thank goodness you've come! I've just been mugged by a man who hit me with a bunch of flowers.
DETECTIVE GOLIGHTLY: *Aha! It was robbery with violets, was it?*

BASHER BATES: If you're *really* a police officer, why are you wearing that blue and green patterned outfit?
P.C. POUNCER: *It's just a routine check, sir.*

Knock, knock.
Who's there?
Hurd.
Hurd who?
Hurd my burglar alarm ringing?

What did the policeman say to the tomato?
'I've had enough of your sauce!'

W.P.C. Perfect was on patrol one day when she passed an elderly lady whom she often saw on her beat. The old lady was limping painfully along. 'What's wrong, Mrs Adams?' she asked.

'My corns are playing me up,' said Mrs Adams.

'What does the doctor say?'

'I haven't been to the doctor.'

'Well,' said W.P.C. Perfect, 'why don't you go and see him? He might be able to do something for them.'

'I've no intention of seeing the doctor!' snapped Mrs Adams. 'My corns have never done anything for me so why should I do anything for them?'

What did the policeman say to his stomach?
You're under a vest!

On what side of the police station should an oak tree stand?
The outside.

P.C. POUNCER: Tell us why you hit the dentist.
BASHER BATES: *Because he got on my nerves.*

What did the policeman do on New Year's Day?
He turned over a new leaf in his notebook.

DETECTIVE GOLIGHTLY: Why have you arrested these hens?

W.P.C. PERFECT: *They were using foul language.*

When do policemen have twelve feet?
When there are six of them.

What do police dogs get when they graduate from training school?
A pedigree.

GIRL: My dad wrote a book called *How Not to Pay Your Taxes.*
BOY: *And is he writing another?*
GIRL: Yes, it's called *Coping with Prison Life.*

P.C. POUNCER: You're under arrest.
DOG BREEDER: *Why?*
P.C. POUNCER: Because these dogs are fakes.
DOG BREEDER: *Oh, no they're not!*
P.C. POUNCER: Yes they are – they're shampoodles.

Did you hear about the man who found a way of turning potatoes into gunpowder? He made a bomb!

P.C. POUNCER: What did I tell you I'd do if I caught you smoking again?
SALLY: *That's strange–I can't remember either.*

P.C. POUNCER: Why did you smash up your office?
SMASHER SMITH: *Something the boss said.*
P.C. POUNCER: Was he insulting?
SMASHER SMITH: *No, not really.*
P.C. POUNCER: What did he say to you, then?
SMASHER SMITH: *'You're sacked!'*

Once upon a time a travelling cinema show arrived in a Wild West town and put on a display of silent movies. All the residents went to watch it, and in the front row sat a little boy eating sweets from a paper bag. 'You're under arrest!' said the sheriff after a few minutes.

'What's the charge?' asked the boy as the sheriff locked him into a cell.

'Rustlin'.'

JUDGE WRIGHT: The next person to shout in court will be thrown out.
PRISONER PETE: *Yippee!*

'Hello, Operator,' cried Burglar Bill, 'can you give me the telephone number for Interpol? I need it urgently—it's an emergency.'

'I'm sorry, sir,' said the operator, 'I don't have the number. Try the London operator.'

So Burglar Bill dialled the London operator. 'Hello, Operator,' he cried. 'Can you get me the number for Interpol? I need it in a hurry.'

'I'm sorry, sir,' said the London operator, 'but I don't have the number. Why not try the Paris operator?'

So Burglar Bill rang the Paris operator. '*Bonjour*, Operator,' he cried, 'can you give me the number for Interpol?'

'*Oui, monsieur*,' said the operator. 'It is Paris 999.'

'Thank you!' cried Burglar Bill and he dialled the number.

'Allo, zis is Interpol,' said a voice on the line.

'At last!' cried Burglar Bill. 'Look, it's an emergency. I've forgotten my wife's birthday so I want you to send her a dozen red roses this minute!'

NEWSFLASH! NEWSFLASH! Police have asked the passengers taking the 10.30 pm train from Paddington to kindly bring it back.

P.C. Pouncer was on patrol one day when he came across two boys fighting in the street. 'Now look, lads,' he said, stepping between them, 'stop fighting! You'll have to learn to give and take.'

'But we do,' said one of the boys. 'He took my sweets and I gave him a punch.'

What did the policeman say to the three-headed monster?
'*Ello, ello, ello*!'

DETECTIVE GOLIGHTLY: Sneaky Sid is a liar and a cheat!
W.P.C. PERFECT: *He's improving*!

What runs right round the police station but never moves?
A fence.

W.P.C. PERFECT: Answer the phone.
P.C. POUNCER: *But it's not ringing*!
W.P.C. PERFECT: Must you leave everything to the last minute?

NEWSFLASH! NEWSFLASH! A lorry carrying marshmallows has collided with a van carrying treacle on the M1. Police are advising motorists to stick to their lanes.

Have you heard about the latest burglar-proof houses? They're called Surelock Homes.

What should you do if you lose your budgie?
Send for the Flying Squad.

DETECTIVE GOLIGHTLY: Why don't you play Monopoly with W.P.C. Perfect any more?
P.C. POUNCER: *Would you play Monopoly with someone who cheats?*
DETECTIVE GOLIGHTLY: No.
P.C. POUNCER: *And neither will she.*

Detective Golightly had been called to the scene of an accident. 'So you're telling me that your father went down the garden to cut a cabbage for your dinner. While he was doing it he slipped and stabbed himself.'

'That's right,' said the daughter.

'What did your mother do?'

'She opened a tin of carrots.'

What happened to the man who smashed the clock?
He was accused of killing time.

JUDGE WRIGHT: Why did you steal that bird?
BURGLAR BILL: *Just for a lark.*

What did Judge Wright say to the dentist?
'Do you promise to tell the tooth, the whole tooth and nothing but the tooth?'

Why are guidebooks like P.C. Pouncer's hand-cuffs?
Because they're for tourists (two wrists).

Lord and Lady Luvaduck were in bed one night at Luvaduck Hall, when they heard a noise downstairs. 'Help! There's a burglar in the kitchen!' said Lady Luvaduck. 'And he's eating the cake cook made for tea tomorrow!'

'Go back to sleep,' said Lord Luvaduck. 'I'll bury him in the morning.'

What do policemen have in their sandwiches?
Pork truncheon meat.

DETECTIVE GOLIGHTLY: How do you spell 'blind thief'?
P.C. POUNCER: *B-L-I-N-D T-H-I-E-F.*
DETECTIVE GOLIGHTLY: Wrong! A blind thief has no eyes!

How did the chimp escape from its prison cell?
It used a monkey wrench.

NEWSFLASH! NEWSFLASH! At today's sheepdog trials Shep and Dash were found not guilty but Rover was sentenced to a month in kennels.

What kind of pudding do lawyers like best? *Sue-it pudding*.

DETECTIVE GOLIGHTLY: This bank was robbed by a doughnut.
P.C. POUNCER: *A doughnut?*
DETECTIVE GOLIGHTLY: Yes, someone who's crazy about money.

Did you hear about the stupid thief who decided to pick a few pockets? He went to a nudist camp.

P.C. Pouncer was patrolling the street one afternoon when he came across a busker playing the violin. 'Do you have a licence to play in the street?' he asked.

'I didn't know I had to,' said the musician.

'In that case I shall have to ask you to accompany me.'

'Certainly, officer—what do you want to sing?'

Which criminal lurks at the bottom of the sea and makes offers no one can refuse?
The Codfather.

JUDGE WRIGHT: We've heard that Lord Luvaduck's wallet was in his jacket pocket. Will you tell me how you managed to steal it?
PERCY PICKPOCKET: *I charge £20 an hour to teach that, my lord.*

P.C. Pouncer was on the beat when he met a small boy sobbing on the pavement. 'What's wrong?' he asked.

'It's my birthday,' he howled, 'and I got a skateboard and a computer game and this afternoon I'm having a party with a barbecue and ice-cream and . . .' and he dissolved into sobs again.

'But that sounds great!' said P.C. Pouncer, confused. 'So why are you crying?'

'Cos I'm lost.'

How do policemen patrol the skies?
In helicoppers.

Lady Luvaduck woke her husband one night. 'Listen! There's a burglar downstairs eating the leftovers from Cook's steak and kidney pie.'

Lord Luvaduck sat up in bed and dialled 999. 'Who shall I ask for?' he asked his wife. 'Police or ambulance?'

A policeman was escorting a prisoner out of the court and into the police van when his helmet was blown off in the wind. 'Don't worry – why don't I run after it for you?' suggested the prisoner.

'Oh, no you don't,' said the policeman. 'You won't get my hat, you'll just run away. I know what to do. You just stand here and I'll run and get it myself.'

P.C. POUNCER: What's your date of birth?
SNEAKY SAM: *Why do you want to know – are you going to send me a birthday card?*

Where do cops and robbers look the same?
In the dark.

DETECTIVE GOLIGHTLY: We're looking for a man with a pile of leaves on his head.
W.P.C. PERFECT: *And what's his name, sir?*
DETECTIVE GOLIGHTLY: Russell.

Why did the traffic policeman always drive in reverse gear?
Because he knew his Highway Code backwards.

What's the Welsh equivalent of the Mafia?
The Taffia.

What happened to the man who stole a kilo of rhubarb?
He was put in custardy.

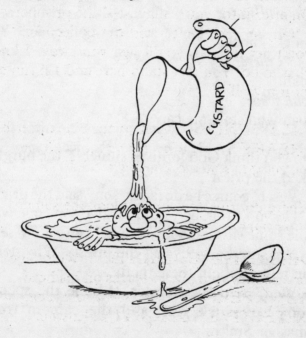

DETECTIVE GOLIGHTLY: You're late again.
W.P.C. PERFECT: *Sorry sir, it's my bus – it's always late.*
DETECTIVE GOLIGHTLY: Well, if it's late again tomorow, catch an earlier one.

P.C. POUNCER: And what gear were you in when you had this crash, sir?
DRIVER: *Jeans, a red T-shirt and a leather jacket, officer.*

Knock, knock.
Who's there?
Noah.
Noah who?
Noah who stole my car?

'Do you think God forgives sinners?' the burglar asked the priest.

'Yes, of course he does, my son,' said the priest.

'Do you think he would forgive someone who stole some silver spoons, a camera and a TV set?'

'I'm sure he will,' said the priest. 'Why don't you tell me about these thefts.'

'Well,' said the burglar, 'I stole the spoons from Luvaduck Hall and the camera from Smasher Smith.'

'And what about the television?'

'Oh, I'll be nicking that from the neighbours' house tomorrow.'

Have you heard about the judge who had no fingers? His name was Justice Thumbs.

DETECTIVE GOLIGHTLY: You've got your helmet on back to front.
P.C. POUNCER: *How do you know which way I'm going?*

What's the best thing to take when you get run down?
The number of the car that hit you.

A robber ran into a building society and stuck two fingers through the glass grille. 'Hands up – this is a cock-up!' he ordered the cashier.

'Don't you mean "This is a stick-up?"' she giggled.

'No,' said the robber, 'it's a cock-up – I've forgotten to bring my gun.'

W.P.C. PERFECT: Oooh! That Sneaky Sid is *so* crooked!

P.C. POUNCER: *Yes, he's so crooked he has to screw his socks on.*

What do you get if you cross a policeman with an octopus?
A policeman with eight long arms of the law.

LADY LUVADUCK: Help! I can hear burglars! Are you awake, dear?
LORD LUVADUCK: *No.*

P.C. POUNCER: Would you breathe out three times, please?
DRIVER: *Why? Do you want to smell my breath?*
P.C. POUNCER: No, I want to clean my glasses.

What happened to the thief who stole 500 elastic bands?
He was put away for a long stretch.

DETECTIVE GOLIGHTLY: The Chief Superintendent has been complaining about your work. What have you been doing?
P.C. POUNCER: *Nothing.*
DETECTIVE GOLIGHTLY: Exactly.

Why did God give policemen ears?
To hold their helmets up.

Who are the strongest thieves in the world?
Shoplifters.

OLD LADY: Does the number 29 bus stop at the river?
P.C. POUNCER: *If it doesn't there'll be a terrible splash.*

P.C. POUNCER: We're looking for a man with a rabbit on his head.
W.P.C. PERFECT: *And what's his name?*
P.C. POUNCER: Warren.

'Doctor! Doctor!' cried the desperate patient. 'I keep feeling this urge to steal things, but I can't bear to go back to prison again. Can you help me?'

'I'll try,' said the doctor. 'Take two of these pills twice a day and you should be cured.'

'Thank you, thank you,' said the patient. 'How can I repay you?'

'Well,' said the doctor, 'if the pills don't work, I wouldn't mind a microwave oven or a video recorder.'

A car pulled up by the side of W.P.C. Perfect as she was on patrol. 'Can you tell me the quickest way to the swimming-pool?' asked the driver.

'Just hop on a number 5 bus.'

What should you do if a policeman sits on your comic?
Wait until he gets up again.

Eight policemen were standing beneath an umbrella and none of them got wet. Why?
Because it wasn't raining.

W.P.C. Perfect was on the beat when she came across a woman sitting in a bus shelter with a baby in her arms, sobbing her heart out. 'What's the matter?' asked W.P.C. Perfect.

'Oh,' cried the mother, 'the bus conductor just refused to let me get on the bus because he said my baby was so ugly. I'm so upset.'

'There, there,' said W.P.C. Perfect, looking at the baby who was indeed very ugly, 'don't you worry about it. Why not come back to the police station and have a nice cup of tea?'

So they walked to the police station and the woman was given a cup of tea and a biscuit. She was just beginning to feel better when P.C. Pouncer walked in. 'Hallo!' he said, looking at the mother and the baby. 'I see you've got some biscuits, but would you like a banana for the little gorilla?'

BURGLAR BILL: We never wanted for anything when I was a kid.
SNEAKY SID: *That's nice to hear.*
BURGLAR BILL: Except for my dad, of course. He was wanted by the police.

Who stole Little Bo Peep's sheep?
The crook she had with her.

NEWSFLASH! NEWSFLASH! A hole has been found in the fence surrounding the Nickem nudist camp. Police are looking into it.

DOCTOR: I think you should take things quietly.
BURGLAR BILL: *Oh, I always do!*

Detective Golightly was walking down the road when he saw a small girl trying to reach a high doorbell. 'Let me help,' he said, and he pressed the bell.

'Thank you,' said the little girl. 'Now run like hell!'

Did you hear what happened to the man who stole a diary? He got twelve months.

DETECTIVE GOLIGHTLY: What is your job?
PRISONER PETE: *I'm a lockmaker, sir.*
DETECTIVE GOLIGHTLY: And can you explain what you were doing in Luvaduck Manor at midnight, in the pitch dark?
PRISONER PETE: *I was making a bolt for the door.*

What did Dr Watson say to Sherlock Holmes on 5 September 1888?
'I haven't a clue.'

Have you heard about the stupid shoplifter? She was crushed under Marks and Spencer's.

31

SAM: Mum, the careers officer told me I should study criminal law.

MUM: *Law? That's wonderful!*

SAM: Yes, he said I have a criminal mind.

DETECTIVE GOLIGHTLY: Why are you late?

P.C. POUNCER: *Sorry, I overslept.*

DETECTIVE GOLIGHTLY: You mean you sleep at home *as well*?

Why was the sheep arrested?
It made an illegal ewe-turn.

What's the best thing to give a seasick policeman?
Lots of room.

W.P.C. Perfect was patrolling Beech Avenue one evening when she met a man crawling around on his hands and knees on the pavement. 'Can I help you, sir?' she asked.

'I dropped my watch in York Road, officer,' said the man.

'Why are you looking for it in Beech Avenue?'

'There's more light here.'

Why is the police football team known as the Scrambled Eggs?
Because they're always getting beaten.

P.C. POUNCER: I think we should legalize telepathy.
DETECTIVE GOLIGHTLY: *I knew you were going to say that.*

The door of the public house opened and a little man came rushing in. He was only five feet high and bristling with anger. 'All right!' he shouted, 'which of you stupid wallies has painted my car pink?'

The huge, threatening figure of Smasher Smith rose from his seat by the bar. 'I did it, shorthouse!' he said, flexing his massive fists. 'What about it?'

'Oh, er . . .' said the little man, 'I just thought I'd tell you that the first coat is dry.'

Which detective loves a good bubble bath?
Sherlock Foams.

P.C. POUNCER: Madam, as I saw you driving down the High Street I thought to myself, 'Sixty at least.'
DRIVER: *How dare you, officer! I'm only 21!*

P.C. POUNCER: I'm sorry, but I'm going to have to lock you up in the cells for the night.
SNEAKY SID: *What's the charge?*
P.C. POUNCER: There's no charge – it's all part of our service.

LADY LUVADUCK: There's so much crime these days, it's a real disgrace.
LORD LUVADUCK: *Yes, it's so bad that even Superman's afraid to come out of the phone box.*

P.C. Pouncer arrived at work one day wearing jeans and a T-shirt. 'What do you think you're doing, Pouncer?' shouted Detective Golightly. 'You're a disgrace to the police force! Go home at once and put on your uniform.'

Half an hour later P.C. Pouncer returned in his uniform, soaking wet from head to toe. 'What's the meaning of this?' demanded Detective Golightly.

'You told me I had to wear my uniform, but my wife was washing it.'

NEWSFLASH! NEWSFLASH! Two criminals have escaped from Wormaway prison. One is two metres tall, the other one metre tall. Police are asked to search high and low for them.

P.C. POUNCER: I'm looking for a man with a hearing-aid.
DETECTIVE GOLIGHTLY: *Wouldn't it be easier with glasses?*

A man was up in court for being drunk in the street. 'Do you admit to being drunk?' asked the judge.

'Oh, yes – I was as drunk as a judge,' admitted the man.

'I think you mean "as drunk as a lord",' said the judge.

'Yes, my lord,' said the prisoner.

DETECTIVE GOLIGHTLY: Our suspect is a man at sea in a barrel.
W.P.C. PERFECT: *And do we know his name, sir?*
DETECTIVE GOLIGHTLY: Yes, it's Bob.

What do police sheep wear?
Ewe-niforms.

Why was Christopher Columbus a crook?
Because he double-crossed the Atlantic.

If tyres hold up cars, what holds up an aeroplane?
Hijackers.

What do you call a burglar who breaks into fast-food restaurants?
A hamburglar.

Which animal commits most traffic offences?
A road hog.

W.P.C. Perfect went to a school one day to give a talk to the pupils. She walked into the classroom and smiled warmly at the kids. 'Now, what shall we talk about?' she asked.

'About five minutes,' came a cheeky voice from the back.

NEWSFLASH! NEWSFLASH! A thousand mattresses were stolen from a warehouse in Barnsley yesterday. Police are springing into action.

Why was the sword swallower sent to jail?
Because he hiccupped and stabbed two people to death.

What did the nude burglar say to Detective Golightly?
You can't pin anything on me!

P.C. Pouncer was telling everyone about his holiday. 'I went to France and on my first day there I rescued a man who'd jumped in the river in Paris.'

'He must have been in Seine!'

Where does Detective Golightly live?
999, Letsbe Avenue.

LADY LUVADUCK: What's the quickest way to the police station?
LORD LUVADUCK: *Run like crazy!*

Why do policemen wear ripple-soled shoes?
To give the ants a fifty-fifty chance.

BURGLAR BILL: Why does your helmet have HITW written inside it?
P.C. POUNCER: *It stands for Head In This Way.*

What did the burglar say when he stole a grandfather clock from an antique shop?
Thanks for your time.

Why did the policeman take a ruler to bed with him?
He wanted to see how long he slept.

DETECTIVE GOLIGHTLY: It's strange, constable, but I always find clues in the last place I look for them.
P.C. POUNCER: *That's because once you find them you stop looking!*

P.C. Perfect was interviewing a suspect. 'Do you have a job?' he asked.
'Yes, I'm a government artist.'
'What exactly do you do?'
'I draw the dole.'

Knock, knock.
Who's there?
Juno.
Juno who?
Juno the time? Someone stole my watch.

How do policemen dress on a cold day?
Quickly.

Burglar Bill was in court for yet another burglary.
'Back again!' complained Judge Wright. 'As
you're such a persistent offender I'm going to
give you the maximum sentence possible.'
   'Don't I get a discount for being a regular?'

P.C. POUNCER: Do you know this is a one-way street?
DRIVER: *But I'm only going one way, officer*!

What was the name of the lawyer's wife?
Sue.

What happened to the woman who threw a bottle of Domestos at P.C. Pouncer?
She was charged with a bleach of the police.

What do jelly policemen wear on their feet?
Gumboots.
And what do they fly in?
Jellycopters.

JUDGE WRIGHT: Did you grow up in a tough neighbourhood?
SMASHER SMITH: *Tough? It was so bad we didn't get marks at school, just bruises.*

What is harder for P.C. Pouncer to catch the faster he runs?
His breath.

JUDGE WRIGHT: Burglar Bill, you are accused of stealing an elephant. Why on earth did you take it?

BURGLAR BILL: *Because when I was young my dad said, 'If you're going to steal something, steal something big.'*

A stupid man had been found guilty of shoplifting. 'You can choose between a month in prison or a £500 fine,' said Judge Wright.

The prisoner thought about it for a few minutes, then said, 'I'll take the £500, thank you very much, my lord.'

W.P.C. PERFECT: Oooh! That Burglar Bill's *so* crooked!

P.C. POUNCER: *Yes, he's so crooked even his shadow's bent.*

Smasher Smith came into the police station one morning and complained that Basher Bates had hit him over the head with a spade. 'I want him arrested,' he insisted.

'When did you say he hit you?' asked W.P.C. Perfect.

'Last night.'

'You don't look as if you've been hit with a spade,' said W.P.C. Perfect. 'There are no bruises or marks.'

'You should see the spade!'

What happened when Batman and Robin were run over by a steamroller?
They were known as Flatman and Ribbon.

DETECTIVE GOLIGHTLY: There's been an escape from Wormaway prison. Look out for a man with one leg called Jones.
P.C. POUNCER: *I wonder what his other leg's called?*

DETECTIVE GOLIGHTLY: Tell me, Miss Smith, why did you stab Mr Jones?

MISS SMITH: *Because he told me my tights were wrinkled.*

DETECTIVE GOLIGHTLY: That doesn't seem a good enough reason to stab him.

MISS SMITH: *But I wasn't wearing any tights!*

What's Woofer the police dog's phone number? *Canine, canine, canine.*

DETECTIVE GOLIGHTLY: Would you like to explain why you burgled the same boutique three nights in a row?

BURGLAR BILL: *It's my wife, officer. She made me go back and change the dress twice.*

A woman and her family went on holiday to Skegpool and on the second day there her son was arrested. 'What's my son done?' she demanded, storming into the police station.

'He was caught standing on the beach throwing stones at your hotel,' said the policeman.

'What's wrong with that?' asked the woman. 'It says it's just a stone's throw from the beach and he was only testing.'

P.C. Pouncer was riding down a lane on his bike one afternoon when he met a hiker walking along with a huge wooden sign saying 'Land's End' tucked under his arm.

'May I ask why you're carrying that sign?' asked P.C. Pouncer.

'Because I'm walking to Land's End,' said the hiker, 'and I don't want to lose my way.'

Did you hear about the man who robbed the glue factory? He said, 'Stick 'em up!'

P.C. POUNCER: Have you met the traffic warden with pedestrian eyes?
W.P.C. PERFECT: *What are pedestrian eyes?*
P.C. POUNCER: They look both ways at the same time.

Did you hear about the stupid terroist who tried to blow up the QE2? He couldn't get his mouth around the funnel.

DETECTIVE GOLIGHTLY: Why weren't you at work yesterday?
P.C. POUNCER: *I was sick.*
DETECTIVE GOLIGHTLY: Sick of what?
P.C. POUNCER: *Sick of work.*

Basher Bates and Sneaky Sid were in court accused of fighting. The lawyers were questioning a witness in the witness box. 'Did you actually see Mr Bates bite off Sid's nose?' asked one of them.

'No, I didn't actually *see* him bite it off,' said the witness.

'Aha!' cried the lawyer. 'So how can you be so sure he did it?'

'I saw him spit it out.'

What goes missing each time Detective Golightly
stands up?
His lap.

What does a policeman do when it rains?
He gets wet.

LADY LUVADUCK: Help me, officer! There's
an elephant sleeping in my bed!
P.C. POUNCER: *How do you know it's an
elephant?*
LADY LUVADUCK: It's got a big E on its
pyjamas!

How can you make a tall policeman short?
Get him to lend you all his money.

W.P.C. PERFECT: Would you say that a forger
does a lot of good?
DETECTIVE GOLIGHTLY: *No. Why, would
you?*
W.P.C. PERFECT: Well, you must admit he's
always writing wrongs . . .

P.C. POUNCER: My police dog's got no nose.
DETECTIVE GOLIGHTLY: *How does he smell?*
P.C. POUNCER: Awful!

What's navy blue, red and white all over?
A sunburned policeman.

P.C. POUNCER: Help! The thief has escaped!
DETECTIVE GOLIGHTLY: *But I thought you were guarding the exit?*
P.C. POUNCER: I was, but he got away through the entrance.

What's the definition of a criminal?
Someone who gets caught.

NEWSFLASH! NEWSFLASH! A murderer has escaped from Wormaway prison in a helicopter. Police are setting up roadblocks.

SNEAKY SID: Did you hear about the judge who was only four feet tall?
SMASHER SMITH: *No.*
SNEAKY SID: He was just a small thing sent to try us.

P.C. Pouncer called round to see a man. 'I'm sorry to have to tell you that we've had complaints from the Post Office about your dog. He's been chasing the postman on his bike.'

'That's a load of rubbish,' said the man. 'My dog can't even ride a bike.'

DETECTIVE GOLIGHTLY: Do you admit to stealing these ten bottles of toilet water?
BURGLAR BILL: *No, that water came from my very own toilet.*

How can you tell if a policeman's been in your fridge?
Look for size 13 footprints in the butter.

Judge Wright looked down at the little old lady standing in the dock. 'Tell me,' he said gently, 'why did you steal Lady Luvaduck's purse?'

'Because I hadn't been well, your honour,' whispered the little old lady, 'and I thought the change might do me good.'

What do traffic wardens have in their sandwiches?
Traffic jam.

What do thieves eat for lunch?
Beefburglars.

A burglar walked into a pawnbroker's shop and held out a gun. 'Give me the money in your till!' he instructed.

'That's a very nice gun,' said the pawnbroker. 'I'll give you £10 for it.'

Why is it illegal to whisper?
Because it isn't aloud.

LADY LUVADUCK: I keep receiving these horrid anonymous letters.
DETECTIVE GOLIGHTLY: *Oh, who are they from?*

PRISONER 2837464: How long are you in for?
PRISONER 5490687: *I was sentenced to 150 years.*
PRISONER 2837464: Still, lucky you didn't get life.

How does a policeman scold a bad elephant?
He says, 'Tusk, tusk!'

W.P.C. PERFECT: Woofer's eating the station logbook!
P.C. POUNCER: *Don't worry. I'll take the words out of his mouth.*

NEWSFLASH! NEWSFLASH! Thieves have stolen 500 wigs from a warehouse in Wigan. Police are requested to comb the area.

Why did the peanut go to the police?
Because he'd been assaulted.

What do you call a policeman with an encyclo-
paedeia in his trouser pocket?
Smarty-pants.

P.C. POUNCER: Have you heard that thieves
raided the Ritz Motel and stole everything but the
soap and towels?
DETECTIVE GOLIGHTLY: *The dirty rotten
thieves!*

Three people were travelling to work on a train and got into a discussion about why British Rail wasn't making any money.

'It's bad management, that's what it is,' said one man. 'I'm a bank manager, so I should know.'

'I think it's the dirt and the mess,' said a woman. 'Just look at it. Any housewife would be ashamed if her house was as mucky as this.'

'Well, I think it's because the trains are always late,' said the second man. At that moment the woman looked up.

'The ticket collector's coming!' she squealed, and all three of them made a dash for the loo and locked themselves in.

Why do policemen wear navy blue uniforms?
So they're not mistaken for strawberries.

P.C. POUNCER: I'd like half an hour off so that I can get my hair cut, sir.
DETECTIVE GOLIGHTLY: *No – have it cut during your time off.*
P.C. POUNCER: But it grows while I'm at work, sir.
DETECTIVE GOLIGHTLY: *But it doesn't do all its growing while you're at work, constable.*
P.C. POUNCER: Maybe, but then I'm not having all my hair cut off!

The trial was over and the prisoner's solicitor went to see him in jail. 'I'm sorry I couldn't have done more for you,' said the solicitor.
   'Thanks,' said the prisoner, 'but five years is *quite* enough.'

DETECTIVE GOLIGHTLY: I hear you missed work yesterday, constable.
W.P.C. PERFECT: *Not for a minute, sir.*

What happened to the cyclist who was arrested for riding without enough care and attention?
They confiscated his bicycle clips.

LADY LUVADUCK: I've just crashed our terribly expensive car.
LORD LUVADUCK: *Well, that's the way Mercedes Benz.*

What do Hawaiian policemen say when they catch a crook?
'*Aloha, aloha, aloha*!'

What do you call a policeman with cotton wool in his ears?
Anything you like – he can't hear you.

Burglar Bill was charged with robbing a jewellery shop and had to find a solicitor to defend him in court. 'I'll handle your case,' said one solicitor, 'but only if you swear you're innocent and guarantee to pay me a fee of £500.'

'Okay,' said Bill, 'but will you accept £100 cash, two watches, a diamond ring and a pearl necklace?'

What did the policeman say to the naughty frog?
'You'd better just hop it!'

P.C. POUNCER: Every day Woofer and I go for a tramp in the woods.
DETECTIVE GOLIGHTLY: *Does Woofer like it?*
P.C. POUNCER: Yes, but the tramp's not so keen.

W.P.C. PERFECT: Where's Woofer?
P.C. POUNCER: *I had him put down.*
W.P.C. PERFECT: Was he mad?
P.C. POUNCER: *Let's just say he wasn't too pleased about it.*

A young boy was caught throwing stones at a window and taken to the police station. 'Right!' said the policeman. 'I'm going to speak to your dad. What's his name?'

'Same as mine,' said the boy.

'No, his Christian name,' said the policeman.

'I don't know what you mean.'

'What does your mum call him?'

'Nothing – she likes him.'

How did the little boy get into the police force? *He lied about his height.*

DETECTIVE GOLIGHTLY: There's one animal you should never play cards with.

P.C. POUNCER: *What's that?*

DETECTIVE GOLIGHTLY: A cheetah.

Why do secret policemen paint their heads yellow?

So they can hide in custard.

MRS BILL: I've run out of cash.

BURGLAR BILL: *Don't worry – I'll go and get some more when the bank has closed.*

MAN: Doctor, doctor! My eyesight is getting terrible.
W.P.C. PERFECT: *I'm sorry, sir, but this is the police station.*

What kind of exams do police horses take?
Hay levels.

Where do secret policemen do their shopping?
At the snoopermarket.

P.C. Pouncer went to be measured up for a new uniform. In the workroom he saw a man hanging from the centre of the ceiling by one arm.

'What's he up there for?' he asked the tailor.

'Ignore him,' said the tailor, 'he's quite mad. He thinks he's a lightbulb.'

'Why don't you get him down from there?' asked Pouncer. The tailor looked shocked.

'How am I supposed to work in the dark?'

The great detective Sherlock Holmes was eating his porridge one winter morning when Doctor Watson came downstairs for breakfast. 'Good morning, Watson,' said Holmes. 'But tell me, my friend, don't you think the weather is still a little too chilly for you to leave off your red flannel long-johns?'

Doctor Watson was stunned. 'Holmes,' he said, 'I know that you're the greatest detective in the world but how on earth did you know that this morning I decided not to put on my red flannel long-johns?'

'Elementary, my dear Watson,' said Holmes. 'You forgot to put your trousers on.'

TRAFFIC WARDEN: Why did you park your car here, sir?
DRIVER: *It says FINE FOR PARKING.*

What's Woofer's favourite game?
Snap.

What animal does Judge Wright look like in the bath?
A bear.

In the USA a man was about to be executed in the electric chair. 'Do you have a last request?' asked the prison officer.

'Yes,' said the prisoner, 'I'd like you to hold my hand.'

What's the difference between a British policeman and an American cop?
About 3,000 miles.

Which members of an orchestra aren't to be trusted?
The fiddlers.

Why did the woman traffic warden marry the roadsweeper?
Because he swept her off her feet.

W.P.C. PERFECT: The witness says that the thief had a seagull on his head.
P.C. POUNCER: *And do we know his name?*
W.P.C. PERFECT: Yes, he's called Cliff.

TRAFFIC COP: Why were you speeding, madam?
LADY DRIVER: *Well, officer, my brakes aren't working and I thought I'd get home quickly before I had an accident.*

W.P.C. Perfect was interviewing a suspect. 'I'm charging you with stealing a video recorder,' she said.

'But I only took it as a joke,' said the man.

'Where did you take it?'

'To Newcastle.'

'Well, that's taking a joke too far.'

What did the burglar give his wife for Christmas? *A mink stole.*

W.P.C. PERFECT: Woofer just bit me on the ankle!

P.C. POUNCER: *Did you put anything on it?*

W.P.C. PERFECT: No, he liked it just the way it was.

Why does Woofer chase his tail? *To make both ends meet.*

TEACHER: Please come to the school quickly! The pupils are all carrying axes!
P.C. POUNCER: *Is it breaking-up day?*

A policeman was driving along one day when he was overtaken by a car driven by a woman who was busy knitting. He immediately turned on his blue flashing light and chased her. 'Pull over!' he ordered, drawing up alongside her car.

She waved her knitting needles at him. 'No, it's a scarf actually.'

Why was the bank robber strong?
He held up fifteen people.

What's the difference between a policeman and a football?
Try kicking a policeman and see what happens!

W.P.C. Perfect brought a suspect to the police station. 'Does she have a record?' asked Detective Golightly.

'Yes, two Bros albums and a Kylie Minogue single.'

How can you tell when there's a policeman inspecting your microwave?
Because you can't shut the door.

JUDGE WRIGHT: Please explain why you stole the car.
PRISONER PETE: *It was parked outside the crematorium, so I didn't think the owner would be needing it any more.*

BANK ROBBER: Stick 'em down!
BANK CLERK: *Eh*?
BANK ROBBER: Stick 'em down, I said!
BANK CLERK: *Don't you mean 'Stick 'em up'*?
BANK ROBBER: So *that's* why I never get any money!

DETECTIVE GOLIGHTLY: Stop bossing me about! Do you think you run this police station?

P.C. POUNCER: *No, sir.*

DETECTIVE GOLIGHTLY: Well then, stop behaving like an idiot.

P.C. POUNCER: Allo, allo, allo! What's going on here?

SNEAKY SID: *I'm pouring boiling water down this rabbit hole.*

P.C. POUNCER: Why?

SNEAKY SID: *I'm trying to make hot cross bunnies.*

The manager of a shop selling hi-fi equipment was standing behind the counter one day when a man came crashing through the plate glass window. 'What on earth do you think you're doing?' yelled the manager.

'I'm terribly sorry,' said the man. 'I forgot to let go of the brick.'

A thief walked into McDonald's and pointed a gun at the manager. 'Give me everything you've got in the till!' he ordered.

The manager eyed him coolly. 'To take away?'

'All right, all right, I admit I murdered my brother!' cried the prisoner. 'But it wasn't my fault! He was driving me crazy! He kept a pig in our bedroom and the smell was unbearable.'

'But why didn't you open the window?' asked Detective Golightly.

'What? And let all my pigeons escape?'

DETECTIVE GOLIGHTLY: Are you chewing gum?
W.P.C. PERFECT: *No, I'm W.P.C. Perfect!*

A motorway police patrol flagged down a man who was driving without any rear lights. 'What's happened to your lights?' said the patrolman to the driver, who was looking very shocked.

'Never mind my lights!' screamed the man. 'Where's my caravan?'

Which member of the police force wears shoes in bed?
A police horse.

What's the difference between a policeman and a chocolate biscuit?
Have you tried dipping a policeman in your tea?

JUDGE WRIGHT: Order! Order in court!
PRISONER PETE: I'll have a pizza and a cola.

Why did Woofer say 'Miaow'?
He was working in disguise.

DETECTIVE GOLIGHTLY: We're on the trail of a cat burglar.
P.C. POUNCER: *How do you know it was a cat burglar?*
DETECTIVE GOLIGHTLY: Because all that was stolen was a saucer and a pint of milk.

How do Norwegian police send secret messages?
They use Norse Code.

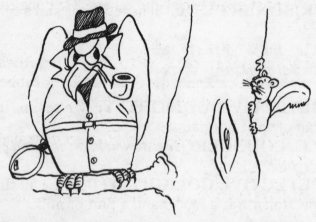

Why is a good detective like a bird of prey?
Because he watches you like a hawk.

A prisoner was planning to break out of jail, so one day when his wife visited him he asked her to bake him a cake with a pair of wire-cutters in. She agreed, but next time she visited him she leaned across the table and said, 'I've got the wire-cutters. There's just one problem.'

'What's that?' asked the man.

'I don't know how to bake a cake.'

What goes tick-tick woof?
A watchdog.

Did you hear about the crook who came out of jail and went straight back behind bars? He bought a pub.

NEWSFLASH! NEWSFLASH! The Royal Symphony Orchestra was held up by a robber today. The thief ran off with the lute.

P.C. POUNCER: Where does that secret policeman come from?
W.P.C. PERFECT: *Which one?*
P.C. POUNCER: The one who always races around.
W.P.C. PERFECT: *He's Russian.*

Which policeman has the best hearing?
The eeriest.

What's the difference between a burglar and a
man wearing a wig?
One has false keys, the other has false locks.

P.C. POUNCER: You were driving this car
when you had the accident?
DRIVER: *Yes.*
P.C. POUNCER: Please tell me what happened.
DRIVER: *Sorry, I can't – I had my eyes shut.*

P.C. POUNCER: Detective Golightly is a cheat! I'm not going to play golf with him again.

W.P.C. PERFECT: *Why?*

P.C. POUNCER: Well, he said he'd found his lost ball on the edge of the twelfth green, but he couldn't have.

W.P.C. PERFECT: *Why not?*

P.C. POUNCER: Because I had it in my pocket all the time.

The phone rang at the police station. 'Hello, is that Nickem 333?' asked a voice.

'No, this is Nickem 999.'

'Sorry to have bothered you.'

'No trouble – the phone was ringing anyway.'

BURGLAR BILL: I opened a hi-fi shop last year.

SNEAKY SID: *Bet that was fun.*

BURGLAR BILL: Not really – the owner caught me opening it!

Why did the judge refuse to send the deaf man to jail?

Because he wouldn't sentence him without a hearing.

Why did the policeman put birdseed in his shoes?
Because he was pigeon-toed.

W.P.C. Perfect came across a small girl crying in the street. 'What's wrong?' she asked.

'I've lost ten pence,' said the girl. W.P.C. Perfect felt in her pocket and found ten pence.

'Here you are,' she said. At this the girl began to sob even more loudly.

'*Now* what's wrong?' asked W.P.C. Perfect.

'I wish I'd said I'd lost a pound!'

Why do footballers wear shorts?
Because they'd be arrested if they didn't.

P.C. Pouncer was walking down the street one day when he came across an elderly man walking along dragging a cardboard box on a dog's lead. The old chap was obviously a bit potty, he thought, so as he passed by he said kindly, 'That's a very nice dog you've got there, sir.'

'It's not a dog,' said the old man, 'it's a cardboard box.'

'Oh yes, so it is,' said P.C. Pouncer, feeling embarrassed. 'Silly me.' And off he walked.

The old man looked down at the box and smiled to himself. 'We fooled him that time, didn't we, Rover?'

'Marry me, darling!' said a man to his girlfriend.

'I can't,' said the girl shyly. 'You'll think I'm being silly, but you've been married six times already and I've been told that you killed all your wives within a week of the wedding.'

'You shouldn't believe what you hear, darling,' said the man. 'That's just old wives' tales.'

P.C. POUNCER: I've arrested these Insect United fans for making a nuisance in the street. They won't stop singing.

DETECTIVE GOLIGHTLY: *What are they singing?*

P.C. POUNCER: Earwig-go, earwig-go, earwig- go. . . .

SAMMY: I've lost my pet rabbit.

W.P.C. PERFECT: *Sorry, it hasn't been brought in. Why don't you put an advert in the newspaper for it?*

SAMMY: But it can't read.

Basher Bates and Smasher Smith were brought up in court on a charge of fighting in the street. Basher Bates was fined £50.

'That's not fair, your worship!' he shouted. 'Smasher Smith bit some of my ear off!'

'Smith is bound over to keep the peace for two years,' said Judge Wright.

'But I can't!' said Smasher. 'I threw it away.'

What do you get if you cross Detective Golightly with a ghost?
A police inspectre.

DETECTIVE GOLIGHTLY: You're telling me that you broke into Tesco's because you were hungry, but you didn't steal any food – only the cash from the till?
ROBBER: *That's right – I always like to pay for everything I eat.*

DRIVER: Excuse me, constable, but how do I get two whales in my car?
P.C. POUNCER: *It's impossible!*
DRIVER: Oh – my map says I just have to cross the Severn Bridge.

There was an announcement in the *Nickem Daily News* the other day. It read: 'We apologise for last week's announcement that Martin Bloomer is a defective in the police force. Of course the announcement should have said that Mr Bloomer is a detective in the police farce.'

W.P.C. PERFECT: I know a man who married his sister.
P.C. POUNCER: *But that's illegal*!
W.P.C. PERFECT: No it wasn't – he's a vicar.

Knock, knock.
Who's there?
Lemmy.
Lemmy who?
Lemmy in! I'm a policeman.

What's blue and tall and shaped like a policeman?
A policeman.

In South America a convicted murderer was about to be shot for his crimes. 'Do you have any last requests?' asked the soldier in charge of the firing squad.

'Yes, I'd like to sing a song.'

'Very well, go ahead.'

'There were nine hundred and ninety-nine thousand, nine hundred and ninety-nine green bottles, hanging on the wall. . . .'

SNEAKY SID: I'm trying to mend my evil ways.

W.P.C. PERFECT: *You always say that, but the stitches still keep breaking.*

HIGHWAYMAN: Your money or your life!
TRAVELLER: *You'd better shoot me – I need the money for my old age.*

Knock, knock.
Who's there?
Don.
Don who?
Don mess about, it's the police!

BURGLAR BILL: What kind of dog is that?
P.C. POUNCER: *It's a police dog.*
BURGLAR BILL: It doesn't look anything like a police dog to me.
P.C. POUNCER: *That's because it's a plain clothes police dog.*

NEWSFLASH! NEWSFLASH! Pete Shoe-string, the TV detective, has gone missing. New Scotland Yard say they hope to unravel the mystery and have the case tied up soon.

W.P.C. PERFECT: Why did you push your friend under a steamroller?
SMASHER SMITH: *Because I've always wanted a flatmate.*

Knock, knock.
Who's there?
Betty.
Betty who?
Betty didn't think he'd get caught!

It was the day of the Nickem versus Copley police cricket match, and P.C. Pouncer had just gone in to bat when Detective Golightly telephoned the cricket pavilion to speak to him.

'He's just gone to the wicket,' said the policeman taking the call.

'I'll hold the line then,' said Detective Golightly.

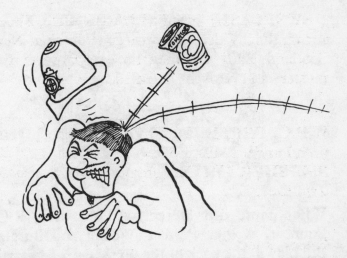

DETECTIVE GOLIGHTLY: Where did you get that bump on the head?

P.C. POUNCER: *Someone threw tomatoes at me.*

DETECTIVE GOLIGHTLY: How did tomatoes cause a bump like that?

P.C. POUNCER: *They were in a can.*

JUDGE WRIGHT: Do you plead guilty or not guilty of begging?

BASHER BATES: *Half guilty.*

JUDGE WRIGHT: And what does that mean?

BASHER BATES: *Well, I admit I did ask the lady for 20p for a cup of tea, but she didn't give it to me.*

What game did Detective Golightly, P.C. Pouncer, W.P.C. Perfect, Woofer and Burglar Bill play in the back of the police car?
Squash.

Which policeman has the biggest shoes?
The one with the biggest feet.

JUDGE WRIGHT: Do you still insist you're not guilty, even though three witnesses have been produced to say they saw you?
SMASHER SMITH: *I can produce millions of people who didn't.*

Did you hear about the bank robber who changed his mind and put the money back? He was generous to a vault.

What are policemen's favourite books?
Detective Stories by Watts E. Dunn
How to Get Rich by Robin Banks
Who Killed the Butler? by Howard I. Know
You're Under Arrest by Laura Norder
The Story of a Highwayman by Anne Dover
The Breakout by Freda Convict
How to Rob Banks by Hans Upp
Safe-blowing for Beginners by Dina Mite
How to Forge Cheques by Mike O'Million

Why was Woofer arrested?
'Cos he walked past the flea circus and stole the show.

91

P.C. POUNCER: Woofer's a one-man dog.

W.P.C. PERFECT: *Really*?

P.C. POUNCER: Yes, I'm the only man he bites.

Which vegetable was arrested for doing 100 mph in a built-up area?

A lettuce Elan.

DETECTIVE GOLIGHTLY: I wish you'd pay me a little attention.

P.C. POUNCER: *I'm paying as little as I can.*

'What are you doing, my lord?' asked Detective Golightly when he saw Lord Luvaduck spreading white powder in Nickem High Street.

'I'm putting down some anti-crocodile powder,' replied Lord Luvaduck.

'But there aren't any crocodiles in Nickem!'

'That's because the powder works!'

W.P.C. PERFECT: We've just had news that a set of traffic lights has been stolen from South Street.

DETECTIVE GOLIGHTLY: *Some crooks will stop at nothing*!

W.P.C. PERFECT: Why is Woofer wagging his tail at me like that?
P.C. POUNCER: *Because you're eating out of his bowl.*

Did you hear about the man who was such a terrible driver that he painted one side of his car green and the other side red? He did it so that whenever he had an accident the witnesses would contradict each other.

Why did Sneaky Sid grease himself all over before he went to bed?
He wanted to wake up oily in the morning.

NEWSFLASH! NEWSFLASH! All the lavatories were stolen from Nickem police station last night. Detective Golightly reports that the police have nothing to go on.

W.P.C. Perfect had been out of the police station all day following a woman suspected of being a spy. In the evening she phoned Detective Golightly. 'I followed her to Cardiff,' she said, 'but she gave me the slip. Then I followed her to Bristol, but she gave me the slip. Then I followed her to Swindon . . .'

'But she gave you the slip?' said Detective Golightly.

'No, in Swindon she gave me her dress.'

What kind of bird spends its life in prison?
A jailbird.

Why was the wine waiter arrested?
Because he served wine with a real body in it.

JUDGE WRIGHT: Have you been up before me in the past?
PRISONER PETE: *I don't know. What time do you usually get up?*

LORD LUVADUCK: Last night I shot a burglar in my pyjamas.
W.P.C. PERFECT: *Did you really?*
LORD LUVADUCK: Yes. How he got into them I don't know.

Why do police dogs wear fur coats?
Because they'd look silly in plastic macs.

Judge Wright was winding up a court case. 'I'm not satisfied with the evidence against you,' he told Burglar Bill, 'so I'm going to find you not guilty. You may leave the court.'

'Does this mean I can keep the video and the microwave?' asked Bill.

Did you hear about the robber who always had a bath before going out robbing? It was so that he could make a clean getaway.

Why was the python arrested?
Because it got a crush on someone.

Which painter had the most arresting name?
Constable.

BASHER BROWN: I wouldn't hurt a fly, I tell you!

P.C. POUNCER: *No, it's people you prefer!*

At police training school a young policeman was asked what he'd do if he was driving alone down a country lane when he came across twenty armed robbers all pointing their guns at him.

'Eighty miles an hour,' he replied.

TOURIST: Help, help! Someone just stole my camera.

P.C. POUNCER: *Don't panic, sir. Just wait and see what develops.*

NEWSFLASH! NEWSFLASH! Thieves broke into a chemist's last night and stole a hundred bottles of perfume. Police are on the scent.

Why did W.P.C. Perfect arrest the two elephants? *Because they went swimming with only one pair of trunks.*

SMASHER SMITH: What do the letters CID stand for?

BURGLAR BILL: *Copper in Disguise.*

What kind of buttonholes do police dogs wear?
Collie-flowers.

JUDGE WRIGHT: This is the seventh time you've been convicted for burglary. Aren't you ashamed of yourself?
BURGLAR BILL: *Oh, no, your honour. I always have the courage of my convictions.*

Why were the cows arrested on the M25?
Because their horns didn't work.

What's green, covered in vinegar and holds up stagecoaches?
Dick Gherkin.

What has ten legs, six ears and seven eyes?
A policeman, a police horse, a police dog and a needle.

When are policemen strong?
When they hold up the traffic.

LADY LUVADUCK: We've been robbed by a man with a spade on his head.
DETECTIVE GOLIGHTLY: *I bet his name's Doug!*

SALLY: The police recruiting officer is visiting school this morning.

SAMMY: *I'm not going to see him. I know how to join the police.*

SALLY: How?

SAMMY: *Just tie their shoelaces together.*

Knock, knock.
Who's there?
Dale.
Dale who?
Dale-light robbery.

What's a policeman's favourite meal?
I-arrest stew.

A lawyer was questioning his very nervous client in the witness box. 'Are you married?' he asked.

'Yes,' said the man.

'And whom did you marry?' asked the lawyer.

'A woman,' said the man nervously.

'Well, of course you married a woman – have you heard of anyone marrying a man?' snapped the lawyer.

'Well, yes . . . My sister did.'

P.C. POUNCER: Can you tell me what you're doing dressed in only a copy of a newspaper, sir?

MAN: *I like to dress with* The Times.

Why does Batman search for worms?
To feed his Robin.

P.C. Pouncer was out in the patrol car one day when it broke down in a narrow country lane. He climbed out, lifted the bonnet and looked inside, but he couldn't see what was wrong. After a few minutes a brown and white cow came and stood by the gate. It peered at the engine and then said, 'You've got a problem with your carburettor.' And with that it strolled off to the other side of the field.

P.C. Pouncer couldn't believe his ears. Spotting a farmhouse just up the lane, he ran towards it. 'My car's broken down,' he called to the farmer who was feeding the hens in the yard, 'and a cow just came up and told me that it was my carburettor!'

'Was it a brown cow with white patches?' asked the farmer.

'Yes, it was,' said P.C. Pouncer.

'That's Blossom,' said the farmer. 'Don't take any notice of her – she doesn't know anything about car engines.'

Why did the policeman climb a tree?
Because he wanted to be in the Special Branch.

What kind of bird holds up visitors to the bird table?
A robin.

DETECTIVE GOLIGHTLY: You remind me of a famous film star.
BURGLAR BILL: *Tom Cruise? Matt Dillon? Jason Donovan?*
DETECTIVE GOLIGHTLY: No, Freddy from *Nightmare on Elm Street.*

A teddy bear went to work on a building site one day. He worked hard all morning digging a trench, and at lunchtime he put down his tools and went to the café for a sandwich. When he got back to resume work he found his tools had gone.

'Call the police!' he told the site foreman. 'Someone's stolen my pick.'

'Stop making a fuss,' said the foreman. 'Don't you know today's the day that teddy bears have their picks nicked?'

What country do frozen policemen come from? *Chile*.

NEWSFLASH! NEWSFLASH! The man who tried to rescue a guy from a blazing bonfire last night was described by police as a flaming idiot.

Sneaky Sid was in court for running a man over, a crime that he strenuously denied committing. 'Tell us how you came to get a puncture in your tyre,' said Judge Wright.

'I drove over a milk bottle,' said Sneaky Sid.

'So you didn't see the milk bottle lying in the road?'

'How could I? That stupid bloke had it stuffed in his pocket.'

P.C. POUNCER: They say God moves in mysterious ways.
W.P.C. PERFECT: *He never leaves any fingerprints.*

What did Detective Golightly say when he tracked down Burglar Bill?
'*Policed to meet you.*'

How can you tell what's on the menu in the police canteen?
Just look at the tablecloth and guess.

Why do policemen wear navy blue uniforms?
Because they'd look silly in party dresses.

Why was the chef arrested?
There was a real shepherd in his shepherd's pie.

'Who are you?' asked the frightened couple who opened the door after several loud knocks.

'Police!' said the detective.

'But you're not in uniform,' protested the couple.

'That's because I'm CID.'

'Well, in that case you'd better come in, Sid.'

POLICE MESSAGE: Will the motorist who took the third exit of the M6 please bring it back immediately.

P.C. Pouncer was out on patrol one day when he came to the river where Burglar Bill was splashing around in the water. 'Help, help!' cried Bill when he saw P.C. Pouncer. 'I can't swim!'

'And I can't fly,' said P.C. Pouncer, 'but have you ever heard me shouting about it?'

P.C. POUNCER: Now, which of you gentlemen was driving this car when it hit the lamppost?
DRUNK: *None of us, officer. We were all in the back seat singing.*

Why was the computer expert arrested in the fish shop?
Because he stole some silicon chips.

What do prisoners study in biology class?
Cells.

LADY LUVADUCK: Do you have a ladies' waiting-room here?
P.C. POUNCER: *No, but we have a room for ladies who can't wait.*

What happened to the police dog that ate nothing but garlic?
His bark was worse than his bite.

JUDGE WRIGHT: Did you or did you not steal this carpet?
SNEAKY SID: *Yes and no.*
JUDGE WRIGHT: What do you mean?
SNEAKY SID: *Well, Mrs Adams gave me the carpet and told me to beat it, so I did.*

Two burglars were disturbed as they were ransacking a flat in a tall building. 'We'll have to jump out of the window,' said one as he climbed on to the sill.

'But we're on the thirteenth floor!' protested the other.

'This is a fine time to be superstitious!'

Why did J.R. go to court?
To Sue Ellen.

What did one strawberry say to the other strawberry?
Call the police – we're in a jam.

DETECTIVE GOLIGHTLY: There's only one honest way to make money.
SNEAKY SID: *What is it?*
DETECTIVE GOLIGHTLY: I thought you wouldn't know it!

DRIVER: Excuse me, officer, can you tell me the way to Bath?
P.C. POUNCER: *Well, sir, I always use soap and water myself.*

P.C. POUNCER: I don't know the meaning of the word 'fear'.
W.P.C. PERFECT: *It's not the only word you don't know the meaning of!*

Why did P.C. Pouncer give the smelly tramp an aspirin?
Because he had a stinking headache.

Have you heard about the Eskimo bag-snatcher?
He was caught mugging a snowman!

A taxi driver walked into the police station with a
wooden box. 'Someone left this in the back of my
cab,' he reported.

P.C. Pouncer took off the lid of the box. 'Fish!'
he exclaimed. 'A whole box of it.'

'What shall I do?' asked the taxi driver.

'Leave it with us,' said P.C. Pouncer, 'and if the
owner hasn't collected it in six weeks' time you
can claim it.'

P.C. POUNCER: My bike's started to go round
biting people!
W.P.C. PERFECT: *It must be a vicious cycle.*

Why are British policemen no good at hula-hooping?
Because they have stiff upper lips.

P.C. POUNCER: We've been asked to look out for the man who owns all the cows in Saudi Arabia.
DETECTIVE GOLIGHTLY: *Aha! You mean the Milk Sheikh.*

Knock, knock.
Who's there?
Ann.
Ann who?
Ann dus your money.

P.C. POUNCER: Woofer doesn't eat meat.
SMASHER SMITH: *Why not?*
P.C. POUNCER: Because I don't give him any.

What did the traffic lights say to the policeman?
Don't look now – I'm changing.

Which ghostly policeman haunts pubs?
An innspectre.

P.C. POUNCER: The thief was described as having a bonfire on his head.
DETECTIVE GOLIGHTLY: *I can deduce his name – Bernard.*

P.C. POUNCER: Why did you open the car door when you stopped at the traffic lights?
DRIVER: *I wanted to let the clutch out.*

DETECTIVE GOLIGHTLY: Okay, what were you doing in Luvaduck Hall at midnight, with a bag marked SWAG? I want an explanation and I want the truth.
BURGLAR BILL: *You want both?*

A man rushed into the police station, jumped on to Detective Golightly's back and yelled, 'One! Two! Three! Four! Five!'

'Get off!' shouted Detective Golightly. 'What do you think you're playing at?'

'Well,' explained the man, 'my mum told me that I could always count on the police.'

What do you get if you dial 666?
An Australian policeman.

TRAFFIC POLICEMAN: Do you realize you've been driving at 120 miles per hour?
DRIVER: *That's impossible! I haven't even been out for an hour.*

What do you call a gorilla with a gun?
Sir.

W.P.C. PERFECT: Why don't you put some
more air in your bike tyres?
P.C. POUNCER: *I can't stand the pressure*.

'Police! Police! A thief's just stolen a hundred
watches, fifty bracelets and a pair of trousers from
my jewellery shop!' cried a man on the telephone.

'Can you chase him?' asked the policeman.

'No!' shouted the jeweller. 'They were *my*
trousers!'

P.C. POUNCER: Are you going to come quietly?
SMASHER SMITH: *No.*
P.C. POUNCER: In that case I shall put in my earplugs.

Who's the most famous detective in fairyland?
Sherlock Gnomes.

W.P.C. PERFECT: You're late again! Don't you have an alarm clock?
P.C. POUNCER: *Yes, but it keeps going off while I'm asleep.*

JUDGE WRIGHT: So you're telling me you stabbed your husband 172 times by mistake?
LADY INDOCK: *Yes, my lord – I couldn't turn the electric carving knife off!*

Why was the musician arrested?
Because he was always in treble.

DETECTIVE GOLIGHTLY: I wonder why Robin Hood stole only from the rich?
P.C. POUNCER: *Because the poor had nothing worth nicking.*

What does Detective Kojak write with?
A bald-point pen.

What's the difference between a policeman and a lemon?
A lemon's yellow.

What do you call a polite, honest, well-behaved criminal?
A failure.

Why do policemen wear red braces?
To hold up their trousers up.

Knock, knock.
Who's there?
Police.
Police who?
Policed to meet you.

How do judges relax after a day at work?
They go to the squash courts.

P.C. POUNCER: Which way did the computer thief go?
DETECTIVE GOLIGHTLY: *He went data way!*

Why were the police called to the restaurant kitchen?
Because the cook was beating the cream and whipping the eggs.

W.P.C. PERFECT: What's your name?
BOY: *Andrew Mickey Taylor.*
W.P.C. PERFECT: In that case I'll call you Andrew Taylor.
BOY: *My mum won't like that.*
W.P.C. PERFECT: Why not?
BOY: *She doesn't like people taking the Mickey out of me.*

A robber appeared in court one day. 'Tell me, have you stolen anything before?' asked the judge.

'Now and then,' said the robber casually.

'Where did these robberies take place?' asked the judge.

'Round and about,' said the robber.

'In that case, I find you guilty. Take him down to the cells, officer,' said the judge.

'Wait a minute!' yelled the robber. 'When am I going to be let out of prison?'

'Oh, sooner or later,' said the judge.

What do you call two policeman?
A pair of knickers.

LORD LUVADUCK: Do you have holes in your socks?
DETECTIVE GOLIGHTLY: *No, I do not!*
LORD LUVADUCK: Then how do you get your feet in them?

What's old, grey and got arrested for travelling down the M1 at 100 m.p.h.?
An E-type Grandad.

What sort of soup do policemen like best?
Cell-ery.

Why was the man arrested as he used the carwash?
Because he was on a bicycle.

What's the best kind of robbery to commit?
A safe robbery.

W.P.C. PERFECT: Scotland Yard have asked us to keep a look-out for a murderer who prays in church.
DETECTIVE GOLIGHTLY: *What's his name?*
W.P.C. PERFECT: Neil.

P.C. Pouncer was called out to an incident in Beech Avenue one cold winter's evening. On the pavement stood a furious householder, yelling, 'I don't care who you are, you fat idiot! Get your ruddy reindeer off my roof!'

What did the policeman say when he caught a frog spraying graffiti?
Hop it!

What happened to the boy who ran away with the circus?
The police made him bring it back.

P.C. POUNCER: What's your name?
BOY: *Dad Potter.*
P.C. POUNCER: That's very unusual.
BOY: *Yes, I was named after my father.*

DETECTIVE GOLIGHTLY: Tarzan's been murdered.
P.C. POUNCER: *But how?*
DETECTIVE GOLIGHTLY: Someone greased his vine.

W.P.C. PERFECT: Excuse me, my lord, but why are you carrying that gun?
LORD LUVADUCK: *I'm hunting elephants.*
W.P.C. PERFECT: But there are no elephants around here.
LORD LUVADUCK: *I know – that's why I'm hunting for them.*

Why did the policeman wear white trousers?
His blue ones were at the dry-cleaners.

DETECTIVE GOLIGHTLY: Tell me, constable, which part of a car causes the most accidents?
P.C. POUNCER: *The nut holding the steering wheel.*

If you dug a big hole in the road, what would come up?
A policeman.

Did you hear about the policeman who had an upturned nose? Every time he sneezed he blew his helmet off.

Did you hear about the stupid pirate who never managed to rob anyone? He wore a patch over each eye.

A man was out walking late one night when two muggers stepped out of the shadows. The man put up a fight, but despite his brave struggle he was eventually overpowered and the muggers emptied his pockets. All they found was 26p. 'Is that all?' they said, amazed. 'You put up a fight just for 26p?'

'No,' said the man, 'I thought you were after the £100 I keep in my socks . . .'

P.C. POUNCER: Why is it always so cold when I'm on duty at the football ground?
DETECTIVE GOLIGHTLY: *Because of all the fans there.*

A police inspector and a girl went to the pictures. The girl was the inspector's daughter, but the inspector was not the girl's father. Who was the inspector?
Her mother.

W.P.C. PERFECT: Woofer's eating the station logbook!
P.C. POUNCER: *Don't worry. I'll take the words out of his mouth.*

There had been so many complaints about the food served to prisoners in the cells that Detective Golightly decided to inspect it himself. 'Any complaints?' he asked Basher Bates, who was eating a plate of stew.

'Yes,' he said. 'This meat is so tough I can barely swallow it.' Detective Golightly took a fork and picked up a piece of meat from the side of the plate.

'It doesn't seem too tough to me,' he said, after a minute.

'That's because I've just chewed that piece for ten minutes,' said Basher Bates.

Knock, knock.
Who's there?
Hans.
Hans who?
Hans up – this is a robbery.

DETECTIVE GOLIGHTLY: You have your boots on the wrong feet!
P.C. POUNCER: *No I haven't – these are the only feet I've got.*

What has a thousand eyes and a thousand legs?
Five hundred policemen.

Burglar Bill's wife wanted a new bathroom, so Bill and one of his friends went to steal a bath from a warehouse. The friend went into the building and disappeared while Bill kept watch. Hours went by, so finally Bill went into the warehouse to look for his pal.

'What's taking so long?' he asked.

'Well,' said his friend, 'you told me to take a bath, but I can't find a towel anywhere.'

What did one pickpocket say to the other?
Every crowd has a silver lining.

JUDGE WRIGHT: I understand it took five policemen to lock you up, you were so drunk last night.
BASHER BATES: *That's right, your worship, but it would only take one policeman to let me out again.*

What happened when the skunk robbed a bank?
Police were soon on his scent.

NEWSFLASH! NEWSFLASH! A lorryload of prunes was stolen from a supermarket depot last night. Police say the thieves are still on the run.

Why do policemen carry truncheons?
Because truncheons can't walk.

DETECTIVE GOLIGHTLY: I'm not myself today.
W.P.C. PERFECT: *Yes, I noticed the improvement.*

NEWSFLASH! NEWSFLASH! There has been an explosion at the paint factory. Police say it was caused when a tank of red paint was accidentally mixed with a tank of blue paint. Twenty workers have been marooned in the building.

LADY LUVADUCK: Can you start my car for me, constable?

P.C. POUNCER: *No, your ladyship. Your battery is flat.*

LADY LUVADUCK: Oh dear! What shape should it be?

What do you call a woman who goes round stealing lavatories?
Lulu.

DETECTIVE GOLIGHTLY: Arrest the photographer!

W.P.C. PERFECT: *Why?*

DETECTIVE GOLIGHTLY: He's just shot a man, and now he's going to blow someone else up!

SNEAKY SID: Doctor, doctor! Everyone thinks I'm a liar.
DOCTOR: *I don't believe you.*

Every day when she was on patrol W.P.C. Perfect passed a man sitting on a bench with a bottle of beer in his hand. After a few weeks she decided to have a word with him. 'You're always sitting here,' she said, 'and you're always drunk. Why do you drink so much?'

'It's because I have a problem, constable,' said the man sadly.

'What's the problem?' asked W.P.C. Perfect.

'I drink too much.'

What's the last thing a policeman takes off when he goes to bed at night?
His feet off the floor.

P.C. POUNCER: Stop fighting, lads! You should love your enemy.
SAMMY: *But he's not my enemy, he's my brother!*

Why is Batman sad in the autumn?
Because Robin flies south for the winter.

P.C. POUNCER: I have a hunch . . .
W.P.C. PERFECT: *No, you're just a bit round-shouldered.*

Why was the optician's daughter arrested?
Because she made a spectacle of herself.

P.C. POUNCER: Where are you from?
SUSPECT: *Scotland.*
P.C. POUNCER: Which part?
SUSPECT: *All of me.*

BASHER BATES: Lend me twenty pounds.
SMASHER SMITH: *I can't, I've only got ten pounds.*
BASHER BATES: Okay, I'll take that and you can owe me the other ten.

MURDERER: I'm going to shoot you because I vowed that if I ever met anyone who looks exactly like me I'd kill them.
VICTIM: *Do I look like you?*
MURDERER: Yes.
VICTIM: *Then go ahead, shoot!*

Why was the surgeon arrested?
Because he kept sticking a knife in people.

DETECTIVE GOLIGHTLY: What were you before you joined the police?
P.C. POUNCER: *Happy, sir.*

Why is a policeman's job so tricky?
Because his work involves a lot of catches.

What happened when there was a fight in the fish and chip shop?
P.C. Pouncer was battered.

Chief Inspector Potter was famous at the police station for his name-dropping. He was always going on about the famous people he knew, and this really irritated his colleagues. One of them got so annoyed that he issued a challenge. 'I don't believe you *really* know Mrs Thatcher, the Pope and the Queen,' he said. 'So let's have a bet. If you can prove they're all friends of yours I'll give you £1,000 and if not, you'll have to give *me* £1,000.'

So off they went to Downing Street. Chief Inspector Potter had a quick word with the policeman at the door and was let into Number Ten, and a few minutes later he reappeared with Mrs Thatcher, who had a friendly chat with him and then waved him goodbye. 'All right,' said the disgruntled colleague, 'so you know Mrs Thatcher – but let's see how well you know the Pope.'

Off they flew to Rome, and sure enough Chief Inspector Potter walked straight into the Vatican and had a jolly cup of tea with the Pope, who talked to him as if he were a good friend. 'Well, Mrs Thatcher and the Pope are easy,' grumbled the policeman. 'But I don't believe you're a friend of the Queen.'

So back they came to London. Chief Inspector Potter had a few words with the sentry on duty at Buckingham Palace and then disappeared inside. A few minutes later there was a fanfare of trumpets and the Queen appeared on the balcony – and beside her, smiling, Chief Inspector Potter. You can imagine how furious the policeman below felt. And he felt even worse when the American tourist behind him said, 'Wow! Who's that up there with Chief Inspector Potter?'

Have you heard about the new car that's been invented for terrible drivers?
It has a glass panel in the bottom, so that they can see who they've run over.

W.P.C. PERFECT: Your hair needs cutting badly.
P.C. POUNCER: *Well, why don't you do it? You cut it badly enough last time.*

What did P.C. Pouncer say when Woofer fell over the cliff?
'Dawg-gone!'

W.P.C. PERFECT: I see one of your car tyres is bald, sir.
DRIVER: *I'll see it gets some 'air.*

VICAR: Help! help! The church is on fire!
P.C. POUNCER: *Holy smoke!*

Burglar Bill is so stupid. When he saw a notice outside the police station reading MAN WANTED FOR ROBBERY, he went in and applied for the job.

P.C. POUNCER: Tell me, sir, how did you have this accident?

DRIVER: Well, the sign on the level crossing says STOP, LOOK, LISTEN. And while I was doing that, the train hit me.

What did Judge Wright say at the end of a tough day's work?

'It's been a trying day.'

Who was the biggest bandit the world has ever known?

Atlas – because he held up the world.

What happens to frogs who park on double yellow lines?
They get toad away.

BASHER BATES: I know how to make money with no trouble at all.
SNEAKY SID: *How?*
BASHER BATES: You just screw up a £10 note and you'll find it in creases.

SILLY BILLY: How long were you in the police force?
EX-POLICEMAN: *Oh, about six feet.*

P.C. POUNCER: You're a naughty boy, Sammy. When Jason threw stones at you, why didn't you come and tell me instead of throwing stones back at him?
SAMMY: *What's the point? You're a terrible shot.*

Detective Golightly was interviewing a suspect. 'I hear your first three wives died after eating poisonous mushrooms. And yesterday your new wife fell off a high building. Doesn't it seem a bit odd to you?'

'No, not really. She wouldn't eat the mushrooms.'

SAMMY: My parents were very fussy about where I go to school.
SALLY: *Really?*
SAMMY: Yes, only an approved school would do.

A prisoner emerged into the sunlight after six years in Wormaway prison. 'I'm free! I'm free!' he cried, jumping up and down on the pavement.

'So what? *I'm* four,' said a small boy as he walked past with his mum.

'Your handwriting is so bad,' thundered Detective Golightly, 'that I can't read these reports. Why on earth didn't you type them for me?'

W.P.C. Perfect was furious. 'Do you think I'd be working here if I could type?'

LADY: Will you help me look for my little dog with only one eye?
W.P.C. PERFECT: *I'd rather use two, if you don't mind, madam.*

What do solicitors wear in court?
Law-suits.

OLD LADY: Can you see me across the road, constable?
W.P.C. PERFECT: *Tell you what, madam, I'll cross over and if I can see you I'll wave.*

Did you hear about the man who was sent to jail for something he didn't do? He didn't jump into the getaway car quickly enough.

Why is your heart like a policeman?
Because it has a regular beat.

BURGLAR BILL: Doctor! doctor! I keep stealing things.
DOCTOR: *Have you taken anything for it?*

Why is a judge just like an English teacher?
Because they both hand out long sentences.

Which washing powder does Kojak use?
Bald automatic.

Why is it easy to break into an old man's house?
Because he has no locks and his gate is weak.

DETECTIVE GOLIGHTLY: You should join the FBI, Pouncer.
P.C. POUNCER: *The Federal Bureau of Investigation?*
DETECTIVE GOLIGHTLY: No, the Feather Brained Idiots.

Did you hear about the stupid shoplifter? He stole a free sample.

P.C. POUNCER: Did you know that one man is run over by a car every twenty minutes?
W.P.C. PERFECT: *He must be very fed up about it.*

What happened to the burglar who fell in a pile of cement?
He became a hardened criminal.

Mrs Wotsit was called to the inquest investigating her husband's death from food poisoning. 'Can you remember your husband's last words?' asked the coroner.

'Yes,' she answered. 'He said, "I don't understand how the shop can make a profit from these eggs if they're selling them for only ten pence a dozen".'

TEACHER: What is copper nitrate?
PUPIL: *Overtime for policemen on late shifts.*

W.P.C. PERFECT: What's green, hairy, has seven legs and horrible pink eyes?
DETECTIVE GOLIGHTLY: *I don't know.*
W.P.C. PERFECT: Neither do I, but there's one crawling up your back.